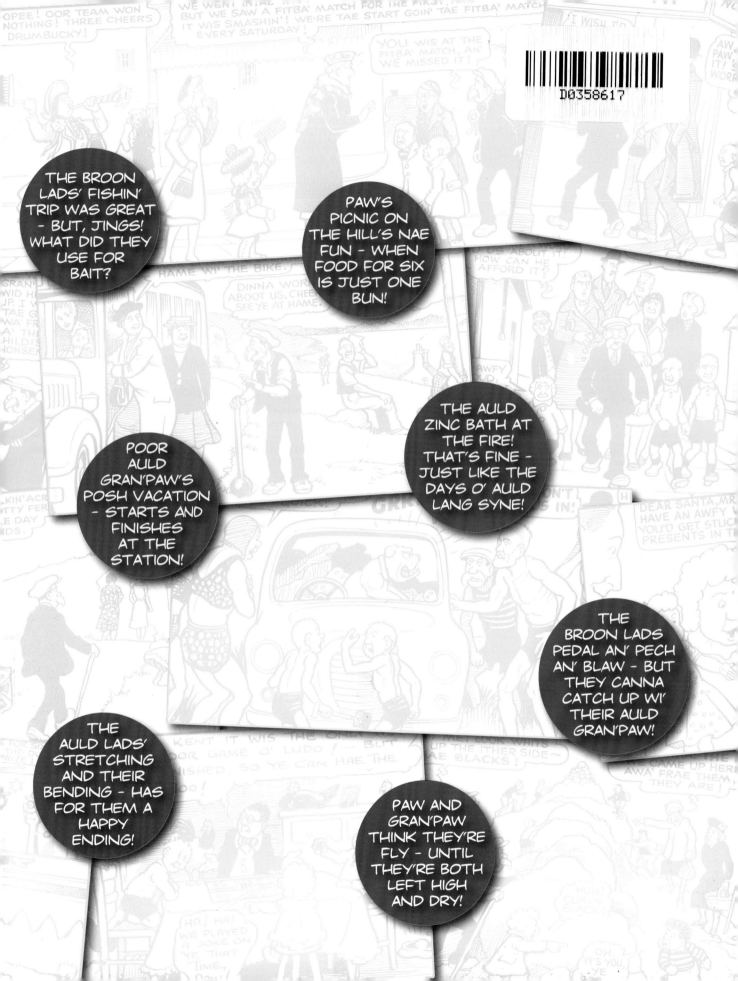

Happy Days!

FAMILY OUTINGS, SPORTS, SPECIAL EVENTS. THESE ARCHIVE IMAGES SHOW A SELECTION OF WAYS IN WHICH FAMILIES HAD FUN OVER THE YEARS.

The archive nature of the enclosed material means that image quality may vary slightly throughout. Some pages may also contain references which are of their time but would not be considered acceptable today.

IT'S GOOD FUN AT THE FAIR – HONESTLY!

PRINCESS MARGARET PICNICS IN THE RAIN

PRINCESS MARGARET spent her eighteenth birthday yesterday afternoon at a picnic on the shores of Loch Muick, despite cold wind and occasional misty rain.

Those at the picnic included the King and Queen, Princess Elizabeth, the Duke of Edinburgh, the Duke and Duchess of Gloucester, the Marquis of Blandford and his sister Lady Rosemary Spencer-Churchill.

The Princess spent yesterday morning looking over numerous presents and reading messages of congratulation.

At tea a birthday cake, with 18 candles, adorned the table. Last night a small party was held. About twenty guests were present. A dance followed.

Princess Margaret is learning Dutch for her visit to Holland on September 3.

WOMEN ONLY IN THE WATER DURING LADIES' DAYS AT THE LOCAL SWIMMING BATHS.

SUNNIEST SPOT IN BRITAIN

FOR the past month Skye has been the sunniest spot in Britain. It has had up to 18 hours sunshine a day.

Mr Donald Maclean, headmaster of Staffin J.S. School, who is responsible for meteorological records on the island, says Skye has been getting nearly two hours more sunshine daily than Egypt.

The island had nearly 200 hours of sunshine last month. Over 100 hours came in one unbroken spell which lasted for eight days.

There's no sign of a let-up, either. This month's outlook for Skye— bright and sunny!

A PEACEFUL DAY OUT FOR ALL, WITH A PICNIC IN THE LOCAL PARK.

A DAY AT THE ZOO COULD BRING YOU FACE TO FACE WITH A YOUNG DEER...
...OR A PARADE OF PENGUINS!

A REALLY SPECIAL DAY OUT IN 1967 SAW THOUSANDS GATHERING TO WATCH THE LAUNCH OF THE QUEEN ELIZABETH THE SECOND LINER AT CLYDEBANK.

Printed and published in Great Britain by DC Thomson & Co., Ltd. 185 Fleet Street, London, EC4A 2HS.
© DC Thomson & Co., Ltd., 2008
ISBN 978 1 84535 359 9

OOR WULLIE   Happy Days!

The Sunday Post 25th April 1937

OOR WULLIE Happy Days!

The Sunday Post 11th July 1937

THE BROONS   Happy Days!

The Sunday Post 27th June 1937

The Sunday Post 24th October 1937

The Sunday Post 19th June 1938

OOR WULLIE Happy Days!

The Sunday Post 10th July 1938

OOR WULLIE   Happy Days!

The Sunday Post 24th July 1938

The Sunday Post 16th July 1939

Happy Days!

FOR MOST FAMILIES, SUMMER HOLIDAYS WERE SPENT AT THE BEACH – WHICH MEANT ICE-CREAM, SANDCASTLES, DECKCHAIRS, DONKEY RIDES AND PADDLING. SUN PROTECTION WASN'T MUCH IN EVIDENCE, THOUGH – UNLESS YOU COUNT KEEPING YOUR COAT ON, OF COURSE.

A HOLIDAY IN SCOTLAND

can be a great success at . . .

DUNOON

HERE'S AN IDEA! DROP A NOTE TO PUBLICITY OFFICER, DUNOON (DEPT. S.P.1), FOR A COPY OF 136 PAGE ILLUSTRATED GUIDE (1/-).

ARBROATH

SCOTLAND'S HOLIDAY PLAYGROUND

Send 6d in stamps for NEW GUIDE BOOK to Dept. S.P. PUBLICITY OFFICE.

— TRAVEL BY TRAIN —

ROTHESAY

Scotland's Sunshine Isle!

ISLE OF BUTE!

In the fabulous Firth of Clyde!

Send 6d. for ILLUSTRATED GUIDE to: Mr N. DUGUID, INFORMATION BUREAU, ROTHESAY

SERVICES AND FARES FROM RAILWAY STATIONS AND AGENCIES

COVERING UP ON THE BEACH HAD A DIFFERENT MEANING IN THE 40s…

…AND THE 50s. TRAVELLING RUGS, COATS AND JUMPERS WERE THE ORDER OF THE DAY.

Right Royal Holiday Cruises

ORKNEY & SHETLAND

from LEITH & ABERDEEN

Enjoy one of the famous inclusive round trips in Company's ultra-modern ships and comfortable hotels from only about £11 to £38. Send 3d postage for booklet.

A SUNNY DAY IN JUNE 1959 SAW A BIT MORE FLESH APPEARING ON BROUGHTY FERRY BEACH. CAN YOU SPOT THE STYLISH SHADES – AND THE HANKIE ON THE HEAD?

PONY AND DONKEY RIDES PROVIDED TRADITIONAL FUN ON BEACHES ALL OVER THE COUNTRY.

SPLASHING ABOUT IN THE WAVES WAS ALWAYS POPULAR.

" We've decided on Dunoon."

OOR WULLIE   Happy Days!

The Sunday Post 24th March 1940

The Sunday Post 8th December 1940

The Sunday Post 21st July 1940

The Sunday Post 1st June 1941

The Sunday Post 17th May 1942

OOR WULLIE   Happy Days!

The Sunday Post 29th March 1942

The Sunday Post 19th July 1942

OOR WULLIE   Happy Days!

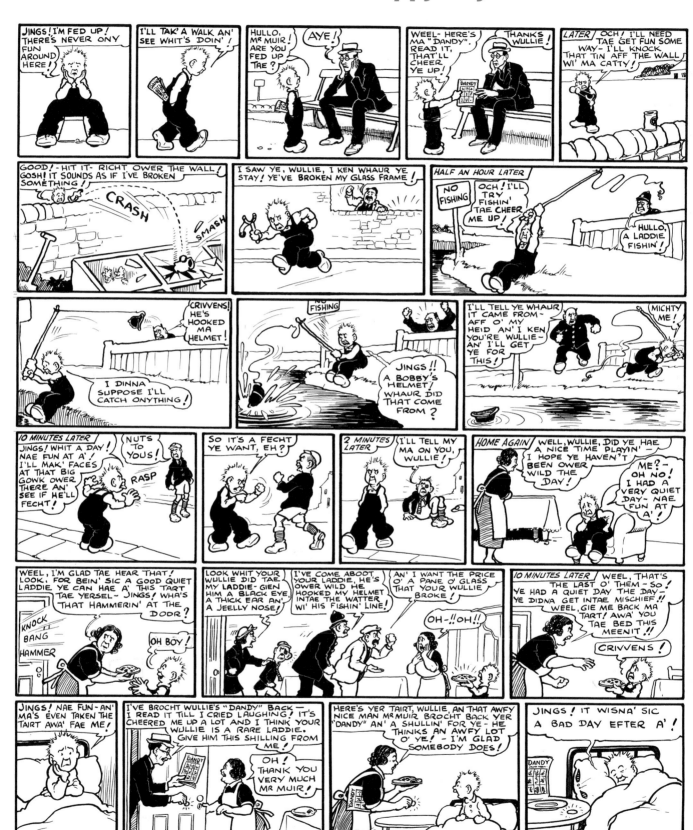

The Sunday Post 28th June 1942

Happy Days!

HAPPY DAYS DIDN'T ALWAYS HAVE TO BE SUNNY DAYS. MAKING THE MOST OF SCOTLAND'S SEVERE WINTERS BROUGHT FUN FOR ALL AGES.

Snow Is The Snag To New League Cup Plan

THE Scottish League clubs will be holding a meeting shortly to endorse the recent agreements with the Players' Union.

All the recommendations of the Management Committee are likely to be OK'd without any difficulty.

There are one or two other points, however, which will crop up and are due for serious discussion.

There is the suggestion — sponsored by Aberdeen—that the Scottish League Cup tournament should be played at the END of the season instead of the beginning.

Idea is that this would keep interest going right to the end of the season.

The only snag is a couple of weeks of snow in January could cause such a pile-up of Scottish Cup, League Cup, and League fixtures, we wouldn't know where we were.

It looks as if we're creeping towards the day when every club will keep its home gates. Several suggestions on these lines are being bandied around just now.

General feeling is next season may see the home clubs keeping two-thirds of the gate and visiting clubs getting one-third. Which would at least be a step in the right direction as far as league reform is concerned.

Meanwhile, league president Willie Terris and secretary Fred Denovan are off to Milan for a vital series of meetings this week.

Under discussion will be the formation of a European league tournament— with representative teams of all the continental leagues competing.

Messrs Terris and Denovan will also try to pin the Italian League down to a definite date for their visit to Glasgow next season.

CURLERS TAKE TO THE ICE ON LOCH LEVEN IN 1959.

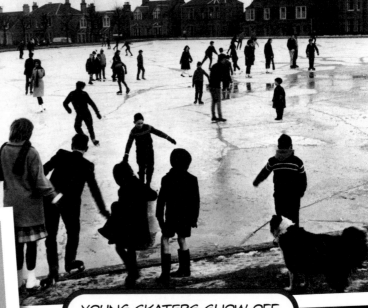

YOUNG SKATERS SHOW OFF THEIR SKILLS IN 1963.

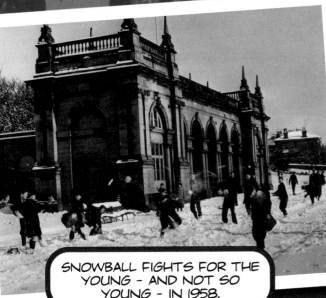

SNOWBALL FIGHTS FOR THE YOUNG – AND NOT SO YOUNG – IN 1958.

YOU CAN TRAVEL ALL OVER IN SUMMER, BUT THERE'S NOTHING TO BEAT—

THE WINTER OF SCOTLAND

BY A SUNDAY POST REPORTER.

NEARLY 3000 feet up the face of Streap, a mountain

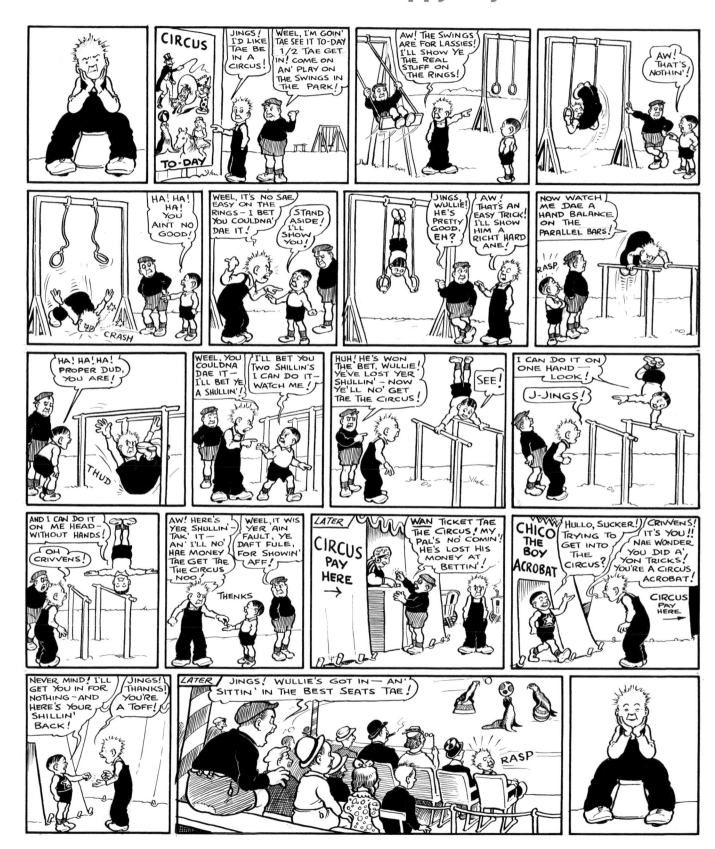

The Sunday Post 15th August 1943

The Sunday Post 25th June 1944

The Sunday Post 23rd July 1944

OOR WULLIE Happy Days!

The Sunday Post 15th July 1945

The Sunday Post 15th September 1946

THE BROONS   Happy Days!

The Sunday Post 28th September 1947

Happy Days!

TIME SPENT AT THE 'BERRIES' OR 'TATTIES' WASN'T JUST A WAY OF EARNING MONEY. FOR MANY PEOPLE THEY WERE ALSO SOCIAL EVENTS. MANY A ROMANCE AND LIFELONG FRIENDSHIP WAS FORMED OVER THE TATTIE 'DREELS' OR BERRY BUSHES.

OFF TO THE TATTIES

Cheery good-byes from girls of St John's School, Glasgow, off for three weeks' potato harvesting at Balhousie, Perth.

TATTIE BRIGADE EMPTIED THE REFRESHMENT TROLLEYS

REFRESHMENT trolleys at Perth station yesterday were cleared out as hundreds of Glasgow school children, who had assisted in the potato harvest, hit the homeward trail.

Their cheeks shining with health after three weeks in the tattie fields, and money in their pockets, the children stoked up for the journey.

Their favourite buy— potato crisps!

A fleet of buses awaited the children on their arrival at Buchanan Street Station, Glasgow.

THESE LADIES BROUGHT A TOUCH OF GLAMOUR TO THE TATTIE PLANTING IN 1949.

BUT IT WAS A BIT LESS STYLISH IN 1955.

TATTIE PICKING WAS FUN FOR THESE YOUNGSTERS IN 1964.

"Ah've got six bairns at the tatties."

SUNHATS WERE ESSENTIAL FOR STRAWBERRY PICKING AT THE HEIGHT OF THE SUMMER - EVEN IN SCOTLAND.

CHILDREN AND FAMILIES TRAVELLED FROM ALL OVER THE COUNTRY TO THE BERRY PICKING. THE LITTLE GIRL AT THE FRONT OF THE QUEUE SEEMS PLEASED WITH HER EARNINGS IN THIS 1955 SCENE.

The Sunday Post 26th October 1947

The Sunday Post 4th May 1947

The Sunday Post 27th June 1948

OOR WULLIE Happy Days!

The Sunday Post 29th February 1948

The Sunday Post 18th July 1948

The Sunday Post 19th September 1948

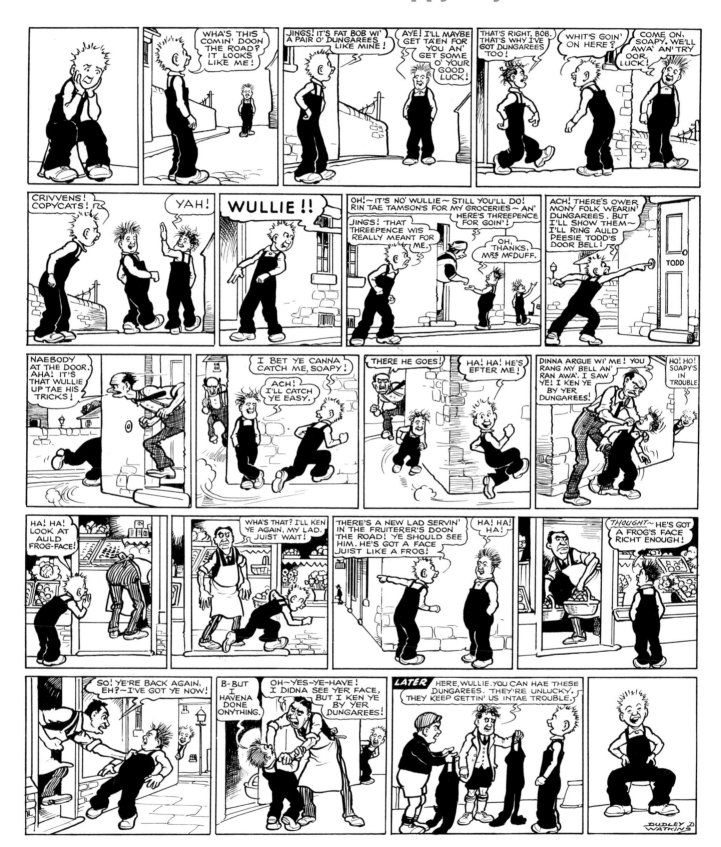

The Sunday Post 28th November 1948

Happy Days!

BEFORE THE DAYS OF LARGE SCALE PACKAGE HOLIDAYS, 'A DAY HERE AND THERE' WAS A POPULAR HOLIDAY CHOICE. UNLIKE TODAY, MANY FAMILIES – ESPECIALLY THOSE IN TOWNS AND CITIES – DIDN'T HAVE CARS AND HAD TO RELY ON PUBLIC TRANSPORT TO TAKE THEM TO THEIR DESTINATIONS.

A DAY 'OOT EAST' – OR WEST – ON ONE OF THE FAMOUS GLASGOW 'TRAMCAURS' WAS A POPULAR EXCURSION FOR CITY DWELLERS.

Cruise Where You Like For £16

By a S.P. Reporter

TWENTY - NINE - Year - Old Michael Shepherd, who comes from down Dumfries way, has loved boats all his life.

Since he was knee high to a

IT'S THE START OF THE HOLIDAYS, AND DUNDONIANS QUEUE FOR THE BROUGHTY FERRY BUS. THE ICE-CREAM SELLER MUST HAVE MADE A SMALL FORTUNE.

A TRIP 'DOON THE WATTER' WAS A HOLIDAY HIGHLIGHT FOR MANY. RESORTS SUCH AS DUNOON, ROTHESAY AND MILLPORT ATTRACTED FAMILIES OVER THE SUMMER MONTHS. SOME FOR WEEKS - AND SOME FOR A SPECIAL DAY OUT ON ONE OF THE FAMOUS CLYDE STEAMERS.

Too Many Holidays For War-Wives
— Says One Of Them

TRAIN TRAVEL WAS A GREAT WAY TO GET AROUND THE COUNTRY. DAY TRIPS TO THE EDINBURGH FESTIVE ALWAYS PROVED POPULAR, AS DID VISITS TO THE SHOPS AND ATTRACTIONS IN A DIFFERENT PART OF THE COUNTRY.

OF COURSE, IF ALL ELSE FAILED, YOU COULD ALWAYS USE YOUR FEET AND TAKE TO THE HILLS FOR A HIKE IN THE BEAUTIFUL AND PEACEFUL COUNTRYSIDE.

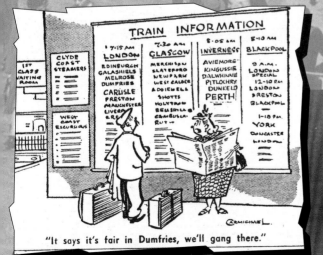

"It says it's fair in Dumfries, we'll gang there."

What A Difference!

NEGOTIATIONS for nationalisation of buses are going on. Feeling in the trade is that when this happens the Transport Commission will equalise bus and train fares.

Here are examples of the difference between present bus and train return fares:—

	Train s. d.	Bus s. d.		Train s. d.	Bus s. d.
Glasgow to Stirling,	8 2	2 9	Edinburgh to Stirling	9 10	3 6
Glasgow to Ayr,	8 2	3 6	Perth to Glasgow	17 5	8 0
Glasgow to Aberdeen,	41 6	19 6	Dunfermline to Glasgow,	12 3	4 6
Glasgow to Leven,	16 3	7 6	Dunfermline to Dundee (via Perth),	13 10	7 4
Aberdeen to Peterhead,	12 3	3 9	Kirkcaldy to St Andrews,	8 2	4 2
Aberdeen to Fraserburgh,	13 1	4 6	Girvan to Glasgow,	6 6	2 6
Edinburgh to London,	107 6	50 0	Fort William to Glasgow,	32 7	22 0
Edinburgh to Berwick,	15 11	8 6			

OOR WULLIE Happy Days!

The Sunday Post 18th September 1949

The Sunday Post 9th October 1949

OOR WULLIE   Happy Days!

The Sunday Post 4th June 1950

The Sunday Post 30th October 1949

OOR WULLIE   Happy Days!

The Sunday Post 24th December 1950

The Sunday Post 19th March 1950

OOR WULLIE Happy Days!

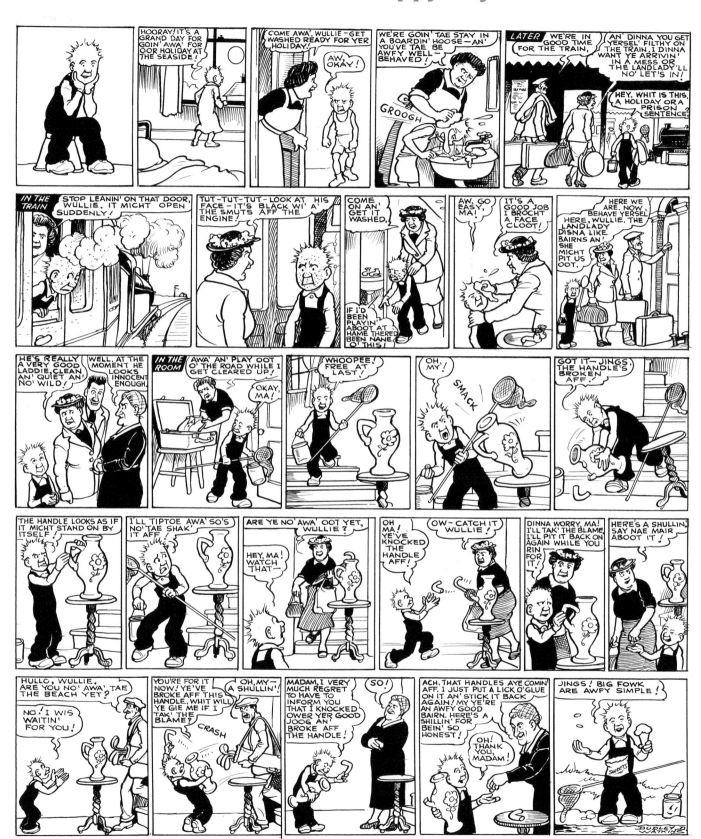

The Sunday Post 29th July 1951

The Sunday Post 18th June 1950

Happy Days! HIGHLAND GAMES ARE TODAY STILL HIGHLIGHTS ON MANY LOCAL CALENDARS. THESE SPECIAL DAYS PROVIDE THE PERFECT EXCUSE TO GET OUT AND MEET FRIENDS – WHILE LISTENING TO THE ROUSING PIPE BANDS. THESE SCENES FROM GAMES OF THE LATE 50s AND EARLY 60s GIVE A FLAVOUR OF THE ACTION.

MARKING TIME AT MARKINCH. THE PIPE BANDS ENTERTAIN THE CROWDS ON A SUNNY SUMMER DAY.

A SIGHT RECOGNISED ALL OVER THE WORLD. TOSSING THE CABER AT THE FAMOUS BRAEMAR HIGHLAND GATHERING.

BEWARE A LOW-FLYING HEAVY-WEIGHT HAMMER AT CORTACHY GAMES.

THERE'S SOMETHING FOR EVERYONE IN THIS SCENE FROM FORFAR HIGHLAND GAMES.

Calling Braemar

A GATHERING of women in **Arbroath** yesterday felt it was not right that there should be no tea served in the overseas visitors' tent at the Braemar Royal Highland Gathering.

They were representatives of business and professional women's clubs from all over Scotland. They decided to suggest to the Braemar Society that tea should be served for the overseas visitors.

Mrs A. Wilson, Larbert, said she understood the overseas visitors' tent was a small one, and there was not even a seat in it. " Many a friendship is cemented over a cup of tea," she added.

Mrs McKenzie, Larbert, said she attended the gathering every year. Last September she went with some New Zealand friends.

She was very disappointed when her friend was not offered a cup of tea or a seat where they could have a chat.

The rain came on, and the overseas visitors were left standing outside. As this was Coronation Year, she felt something ought to be done.

TAKE THE STRAIN! THE TUG-OF-WAR WAS A HIGHLIGHT FOR MANY.

"Ah use ma ain caber."

A REAL "BRAEMAR" IN GERMANY

By an ex-" Sunday Post " Man

WE have just held a real Highland gathering at Stalag 383. It was August 9— about the same time as in peaceful days our " heavies " used to do their stuff at Strathallan Gathering.

do their stuff at Strathallan Gathering.

We were blessed (or cursed) with a real Scottish day. But the pipes sounded fine, and the tartans fluttered gaily.

The Sunday Post 5th August 1951

The Sunday Post 22th April 1951

The Sunday Post 3rd February 1952

The Sunday Post 26th August 1951

OOR WULLIE Happy Days!

The Sunday Post 4th May 1952

The Sunday Post 3rd August 1952

FUN SECTION

OOR WULLIE

Oor Wullie's very keen to go
To see a Coronation show;

And any time admission's free,
Oor Wullie's SURE to raise the fee!

HOW THEY'LL CELEBRATE THE CORONATION IN DIFFERENT PARTS OF SCOTLAND

As part of FORT WILLIAM'S celebrations, the Provost and Councillors plan to lead a procession of townspeople to the top of Ben Nevis. The Provost is to make a B.B.C. broadcast from the top of the mountain. In the evening, Britain's highest bonfire will be lit on the peak.

* *

STONEHAVEN is to have a swimming gala and a demonstration of life-saving by members of the Coastguard detachment. There are also to be trips in a breeches buoy.

* *

Members of OBAN Sailing Club have fitted their boats with sails in three colours— red, white and blue.

On June 3 and 6, admission to ARBROATH'S public baths is to be free.

* *

The Coronation Committee of CRIEFF will start a bank account for every baby born on June 2.

* *

At INVERKEITHING will be the crowning of the gala queen selected by schoolchildren.

* *

To make sure their street will be spick and span for the Coronation, the folk who live in Kinning Street, TRADESTON, Glasgow, are going to scrub every inch of it on the night before Coronation Day. The street is 160 yards long.

As part of the clebrations at FERRYDEN, Angus, two fishing yawls, decorated with fairy lights, will sail up and down the River South Esk at dusk. One boat will give a fireworks display and on the other a choir will sing sea songs.

* *

ANSTRUTHER'S Coronation bonfire will be lit at sea. An old boat, with the bonfire built on it, will be towed out into the Firth of Forth.

* *

Four pipers will sound reveille in Hilton housing scheme, INVERNESS, on Coronation morning.

At DUN, halfway between Brechin and Montrose, they are to have a Coronation television show in a barn.

* *

TAYPORT, Fife, is to hold a special fancy-dress parade with decorated vehicles and bicycles.

* *

In GLENESK a TV set is being installed in the only house with electricity. Mr D. G. Michie, the owner, will keep his house open for all who wish to see the ceremony.

* * * *

1953 WITNESSED THE CORONATION OF QUEEN ELIZABETH II – A HAPPY TIME FOR THE WHOLE COUNTRY. THESE SELDOM SEEN PAGES SHOW HOW THE SUNDAY POST FUN SECTION CELEBRATED THE EVENT.

THE PEERS AND THEIR CORONETS

DUKE—This title comes from the Latin word "dux" meaning "leader."

A Duke's coronet has eight golden strawberry leaves on its rim.

MARQUIS—The name comes from "marches," an old word meaning "borders." it was given to noblemen whose lands were situated near the frontiers of Scotland and Wales.

The coronet has four strawberry leaves and four silver balls alternately round the rim.

BARON—In olden times a Baron was a chief tenant in the service of the King or high nobleman.

On the coronet are six silver balls.

EARL—This ancient title is derived from an Anglo-Saxon word meaning "warrior." Norman Earls were called Counts and their lands came to be known as "counties."

An Earl's coronet is recognised by its eight silver balls mounted on high golden rays with strawberry leaves beneath them.

VISCOUNT—"Vis" comes from the Latin word "vice" meaning "in place of." In ancient times a Viscount held chief office under an Earl.

Sixteen silver balls are mounted on the rim of a Viscount's coronet.

FUNLAND

THE ANSWERS TO THE PUZZLES ON THIS PAGE ARE PRINTED AT THE FOOT OF MERRY MAC'S JOKES.

WHEN WAS THE LAST CORONATION? IF YOU DON'T KNOW AND WANT TO FIND OUT, WRITE THE ANSWERS TO THE LITTLE PROBLEMS BELOW. IF YOU ADD THEM CORRECTLY, THE ANSWER WILL BE THE DATE REQUIRED.

WHEN WAS THE BATTLE OF HASTINGS? HOW MANY — — — IN A GROSS? IN A SCORE? DAYS IN A NORMAL YEAR? YARDS IN A FURLONG? POUNDS IN A CWT.? YEARS IN A DECADE?

THIS LAD AND HIS DOG WANT TO SEE THE SIGHTS OF LONDON. UNSCRAMBLE THE LETTERS ON THE BOARD SO THAT THEY CAN SEE FOUR PLACES OF INTEREST WHICH THEY CAN VISIT.

① DEWSMTISTRNE BEAYB.
② ELWBMYE TDISAUM.
③ ELNOSNS NOLUCM.
④ UHGIMANKCB AAPCLE.

SHADE IN THE DOTTED SECTIONS AND YOU WILL SEE SOMETHING TO DO WITH THE CORONATION.

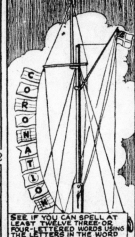

SEE IF YOU CAN SPELL AT LEAST TWELVE THREE- OR FOUR-LETTERED WORDS USING THE LETTERS IN THE WORD "CORONATION."

HERE ARE THREE GUARDS LEAVING THEIR BARRACKS. WHICH ONE DO YOU THINK IS THE BIGGEST — THE ONE AT THE BACK? YOU'LL BE SURPRISED WHEN YOU MEASURE THEM!

THE SUNDAY POST 31ST MAY, 1953.

Happy Days!

THE CORONATION PROVED A MEMORABLE OCCASION FOR THE WHOLE COUNTRY, WITH STREET PARTIES AND DECORATIONS BEING THE ORDER OF THE DAY.

BERNARD STREET IN DUNDEE CELEBRATED THE QUEEN'S CORONATION IN 1953 WITH AN AMAZING DISPLAY OF FLAGS AND BUNTING...

...JUST AS IT HAD FOR HER FATHER IN 1937.

The Sunday Post 6th September 1953

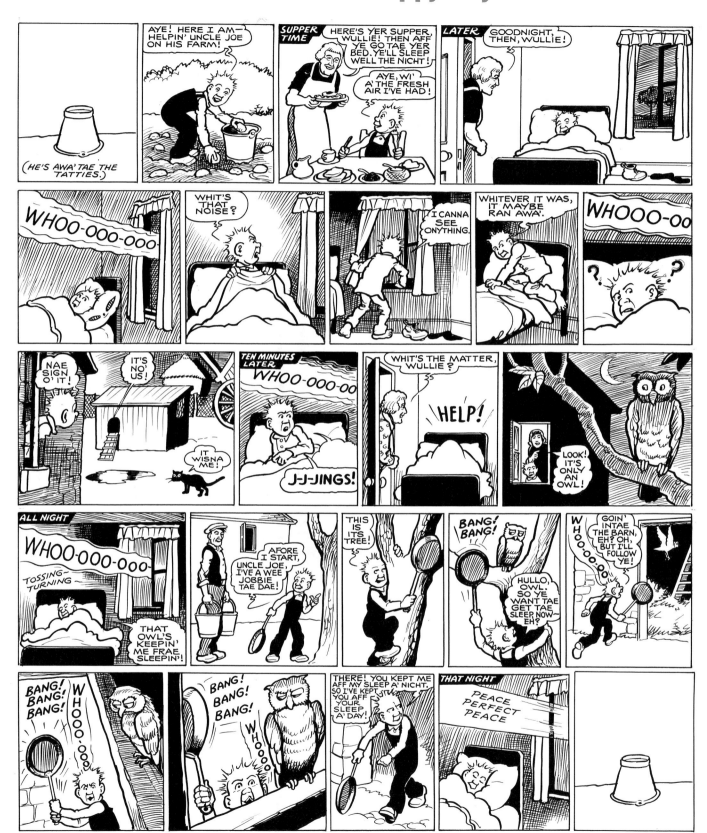

The Sunday Post 27th September 1953

THE BROONS Happy Days!

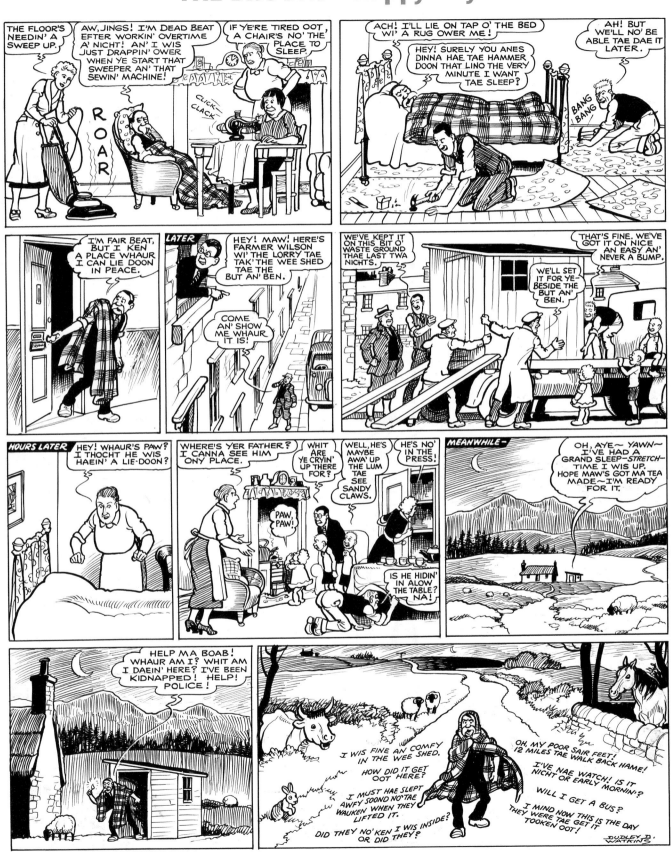

The Sunday Post 13th December 1953

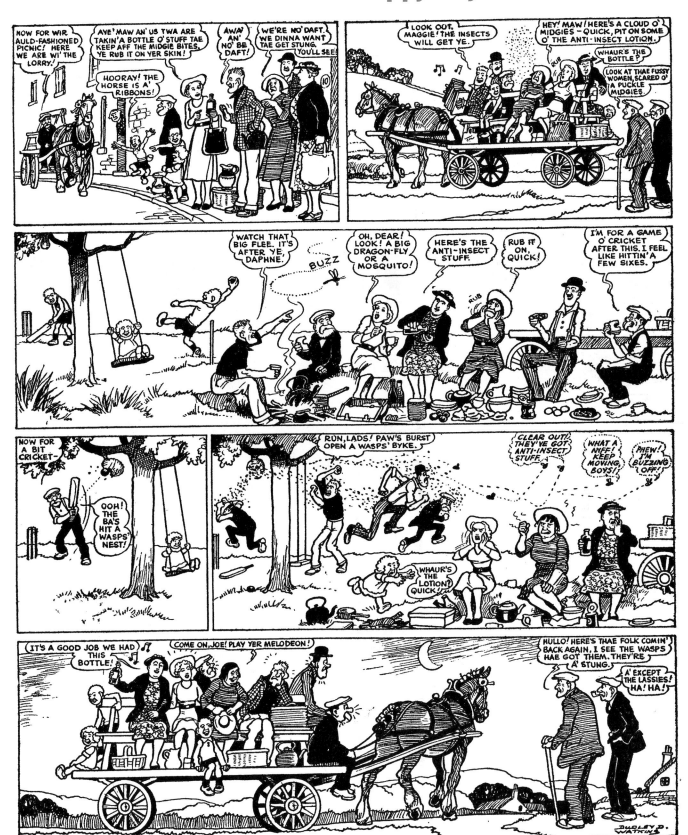

The Sunday Post 27th June 1954

OOR WULLIE Happy Days!

THE BROONS   Happy Days!

The Sunday Post 13th February 1955

OOR WULLIE Happy Days!

The Sunday Post 30th October 1955

THE BROONS   Happy Days!

The Sunday Post 20th February 1955

Happy Days!

TRIPS TO THE THEATRE OR CINEMA AND NIGHTS AT THE DANCING WERE ALWAYS POPULAR. MOST TOWNS HAD A CHOICE OF SEVERAL PICTURE HOUSES AND, IN PRE TV DAYS, VISITS TO THE CINEMA WERE OFTEN MADE SEVERAL TIMES A WEEK.

CINEMAS SHOWED ALL THE LATEST RELEASES AND PROVIDED ORDINARY PEOPLE WITH A GLIMPSE OF HOLLYWOOD-STYLE GLAMOUR.

BY THE LATE 60s, HOWEVER, MANY 'PICTURE HOUSES' WERE BEING CLOSED DOWN AND TURNED INTO BINGO HALLS, SPORTS CLUBS AND SALEROOMS

"If attendances dinna improve, Ah can see us bein' turned back intae a church."

STANLEY WILL STAR IN WEST END COMEDY

SCOTS comedian Stanley Baxter will make his West End stage debut this year.

MANY A COUPLE MET AND GOT TO KNOW EACH OTHER AT THE DANCIN' OR JIGGIN'. THIS PHOTOGRAPH SHOWS A TYPICAL DANCE HALL INTERIOR FROM THE LATE 1930s. COMFORTABLE SEATS, A RAISED PLATFORM FOR THE BAND, PLENTY SPACE FOR DANCING - AND JUST LOOK AT THE STYLISH LIGHT SHADES.

CINEMA and THEATRE PROGRAMMES

ABERDEEN.
ABC—*** Fun In Acapulco.
GAUMONT — *** A Stitch In Time.
ODEON — **** Lawrence Of Arabia.
CAPITOL — *** Dial M For Murder.
MAJESTIC — *** For Love Or Money.

AIRDRIE.
NEW CINEMA—***** Mutiny On The Bounty.

ARBROATH.
PICTURE HOUSE—Mon., ** The Tyrant Of Syracuse. Thurs., *** Marilyn.

AYR.
PLAYHOUSE—Mon., *** Marilyn. Fri., *** State Fair.

COATBRIDGE.
CINEMA—Wed., *** The Errand Boy. Fri., *** The Mongols.

DUNDEE.
REPERTORY—Beauty And The Beast.
ABC—*** What A Crazy World.
GAUMONT — *** A Stitch In Time.
LA SCALA—** Drops Of Blood.
PLAYHOUSE—** Operation Bikini.

DUNFERMLINE.
PALACE — Mon., *** Desert Legion. Thurs., *** Samson And The Seven Miracles.

EDINBURGH THEATRES.
KING'S—Andy Stewart.
LYCEUM—Fol De Rols.

EDINBURGH CINEMAS.
ABC—*** Carry On, Cabby.

THEATRES PROVIDED LIVE ENTERTAINMENT IN THE FORM OF PLAYS, PANTOMIMES AND THE FAMOUS SUMMER SEASON VARIETY SHOWS.

The Sunday Post 30th September 1956

The Sunday Post 7th August 1955

OOR WULLIE Happy Days!

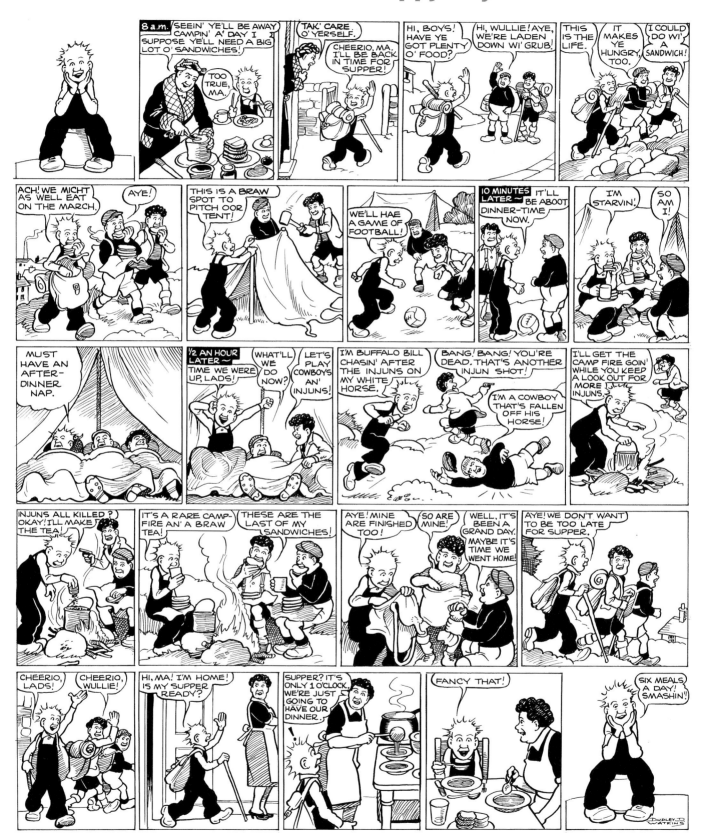

The Sunday Post 28th July 1957

The Sunday Post 21st October 1956

OOR WULLIE   Happy Days!

The Sunday Post 22th December 1957

THE BROONS   Happy Days!

The Sunday Post 23rd December 1956

OOR WULLIE   Happy Days!

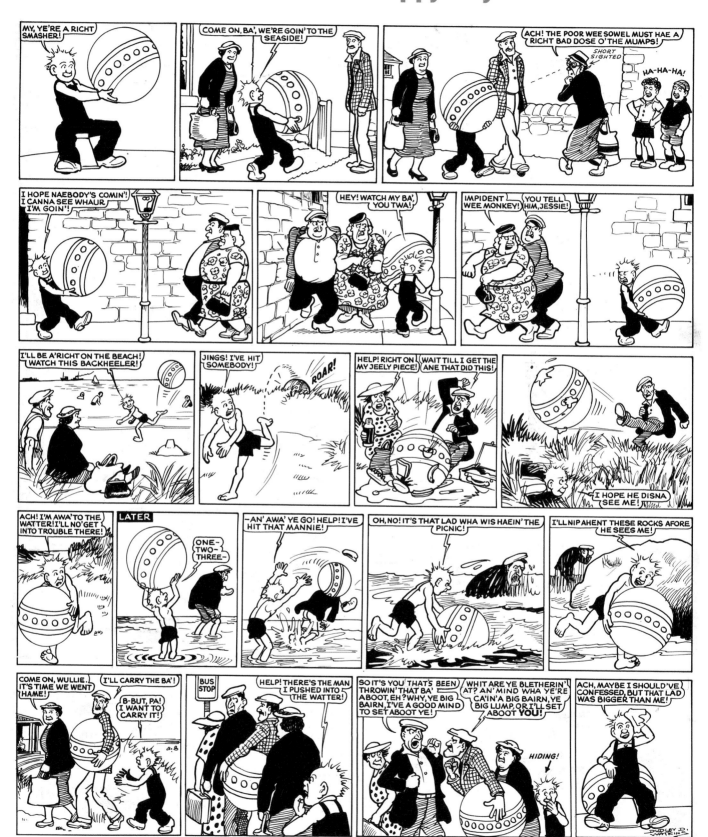

THE BROONS   Happy Days!

The Sunday Post 22nd September 1957

OOR WULLIE Happy Days!

The Sunday Post 16th October 1960

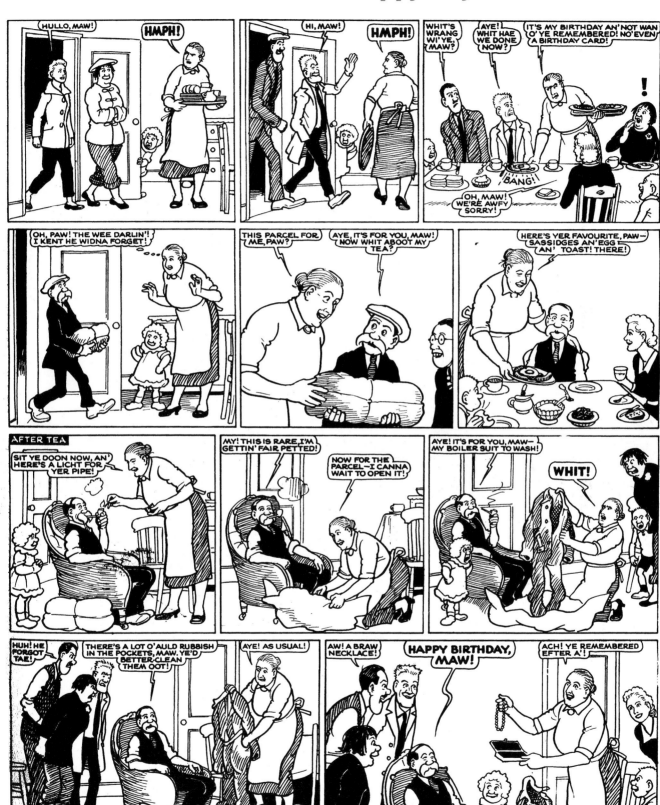

The Sunday Post 11th May 1958

Happy Days!

SMALL OR STATELY, RUINED OR HABITABLE, SCOTLAND'S CASTLES ARE STEEPED IN HISTORY AND ROMANCE. OVER THE YEARS THOUSANDS OF FAMILIES HAVE SPENT MANY HAPPY HOURS SCRAMBLING ALONG RAMPARTS, CLIMBING TOWERS AND RELIVING THE GREAT – AND NOT SO GREAT – DAYS OF OUR NATION'S PAST.

SCONE PALACE DRAWS CROWDS

MORE than a thousand visitors had paid to enter the grounds of Scone Palace at 3.30 p.m. yesterday, an hour after the gates had been opened for a fete.

Such was the demand to see the home of the Earl and Countess of Mansfield that those who paid the 5s entrance fee were limited to parties of 50 for each tour.

The fete is the biggest thing of its kind held by Perthshire Guide Association. A large proportion of takings will be used to send children, particularly crippled Guides, to international camps.

Drawings totalled over £2800.

EILEAN DONAN CASTLE, ON THE SHORES OF LOCH DUICH, IS SAID BY SOME TO BE SCOTLAND'S MOST BEAUTIFUL CASTLE. AND WHO COULD ARGUE WITH THAT?

CASTLE URQUHART, AS FAMOUS ON LOCH NESS AS NESSIE HERSELF, IS ALWAYS A FAVOURITE WITH CHILDREN. THERE HAS BEEN A CASTLE IN THE AREA SINCE THE 13TH CENTURY.

CASTLE FRASER IN ABERDEENSHIRE DATES FROM 1575. IT IS STILL OCCUPIED, BUT VISITORS ARE MOST WELCOME OVER THE SUMMER MONTHS.

TALES OF SCOTLAND'S CASTLES

EILEAN DONAN CASTLE.

Eilean Donan Castle stands in one of the most picturesque settings in Scotland on a tiny islet where Loch Long, Loch Alsh and Loch Duich meet.

For many years, the castle was a stronghold of the MacKenzie clan, which was loyal to the Jacobite cause.

In 1719, a force of Spaniards joined the Jacobites in a rising against the crown. The MacKenzies left their castle to be guarded by some Spanish soldiers while they went to take part in the rising. However, at a battle in Glenshiel, some ten miles from the castle, the gallant MacKenzies and an army of Spaniards, were defeated.

The Royalist commander knew that Eilean Donan Castle would become a refuge for the MacKenzies, so he sent a warship up Loch Alsh to bombard it. The warship pounded the castle until all that was left was a burnt-out shell.

The castle remained a ruin until 1912, when Lieutenant-Colonel John Macrae-Gilstrap started restoration. It was an immense task, and it took 20 years to restore the castle to its former glory.

THE MAGNIFICENT GRANDEUR OF EDINBURGH CASTLE MAKES IT ONE OF SCOTLAND'S MOST INSTANTLY RECOGNISABLE LANDMARKS.

DUNNOTTAR CASTLE, A RUGGED RUIN HIGH ON THE CLIFFS OF SCOTLAND'S EAST COAST, JUST OOZES ROMANCE AND DRAMA.

The Sunday Post 30th October 1960

The Sunday Post 6th September 1959

OOR WULLIE   Happy Days!

The Sunday Post 30th July 1961

OOR WULLIE   Happy Days!

The Sunday Post 6th August 1961

The Sunday Post 29th October 1961

OOR WULLIE   Happy Days!

The Sunday Post 27th May 1962

The Sunday Post 29th July 1962

OOR WULLIE Happy Days!

The Sunday Post 14th July 1963

THE BROONS   Happy Days!

The Sunday Post 2nd September 1962

OOR WULLIE Happy Days!

The Sunday Post 13th October 1963

Happy Days!

FOOTBALL PLAYED A HUGE PART IN THE LIVES OF WORKING MEN THROUGH THE YEARS – AND FOR MANY, THE HAPPIEST SATURDAY AFTERNOON WAS SPENT STANDING ON THE TERRACING WATCHING THEIR TEAM WIN. THE PHOTOGRAPHS SHOWN HERE GIVE A TASTE OF WHAT BEING A FITBA' FAN WAS ALL ABOUT.

GOALMOUTH ACTION FROM THE SCOTTISH CUP FINAL OF 1964.

MIDWEEK CARD

TOMORROW

Scottish League, Division 2—Queen's Park v. Queen of South.

Glasgow Charity Cup—Third Lanark v. Partick Th

Reserve League Cup Final, First Leg —Kilmarnock v. Rangers.

TUESDAY.

International—Italy v. Ireland.

Glasgow Charity Cup—Rangers v. Clyde.

Second XI Cup Final, Second Leg— Falkirk (0) v. St Johnstone (2).

WEDNESDAY.

Scottish Cup Final, Replay—Celtic v. Dunfermline (Hampden, 6.15 p.m.).

European Cup, Semi-Finals — Hamburg v. Barcelona (second leg); Benfica v. Rapid (first leg).

Inter-Cities Fairs Cup, Semi-Final, Second Leg—Roma v. Hibs.

Scottish League, Division 2—Albion Rovers v Alloa; Cowdenbeath v. East Stirling; Hamilton v. Berwick; Queen of South v. Morton; Stenhousemuir v. Arbroath

Reserve League C Final Second

EUROPEAN GAMES WERE ALWAYS POPULAR AND THIS PICTURE SHOWS RANGERS FANS QUEUING UP IN SAUCHIEHALL STREET FOR TICKETS TO SEE THE GERS PLAY SPURS.

30,000 Extra Turn Up At Hampden!

RESULT—QUEUEING, CRUSHING, AND FAINTING

HAMPDEN AS IT USED TO BE. CAN YOU SPOT ANY OF THE BROONS IN THE CROWD?

**ENGLAND 2,
SCOTLAND 2.
Half-time—1-0.
Scorers —
England—Broadis
(18 and 70 min.)
Scotland— Reilly
(54 and 89½.)**

THESE HAPPY DUNDEE FANS ARE BEGINNING THEIR JOURNEY TO WATCH THE TEAM PLAY IN MILAN IN 1963.

BUT IT WASN'T ALWAYS SMILES ALL THE WAY. THIS PITCH INVASION CAUSED PROBLEMS WHEN CELTIC TOOK ON ST MIRREN IN 1962.

OOR WULLIE Happy Days!

The Sunday Post 26th July 1964

THE BROONS Happy Days!

The Sunday Post 21st June 1964

The Sunday Post 27th June 1965

The Sunday Post 16th May 1965

The Sunday Post 12th September 1965

The Sunday Post 3th July 1966

OOR WULLIE   Happy Days!

Happy Days!

AS THE YEARS PASSED, MANY FAMILIES BEGAN TO LOOK FOR MORE THAN JUST A VISIT TO THE BEACH FOR THEIR ANNUAL HOLIDAY. FOR THOSE WHO WANTED SOMETHING A LITTLE DIFFERENT, HOLIDAY CAMPS AND CARAVAN HOLIDAYS PROVIDED THE IDEAL ANSWER.

They're Having a 7-Week Holiday For £4

HOW can a family of five spend a seven weeks' holiday and about two dozen week-ends in the country for £4?

Ask Mr and Mrs Henry Laing, Gardiner Street, Dundee, and their three boys. They do it.

In 1946 Mr Laing, a sheet metal worker, got permission from his boss to spend his spare time making an aluminium caravan on the firm's premises.

He was helped by his brother and brother-in-law. In ten months the caravan was ready.

It's really a miniature prefab, measuring 12 feet by 6¼ feet by 7 feet. A sofa unfolds to become a double bed. There's a cylinder gas stove, built-in cupboards, long windows, even a fire extinguisher.

The whole thing, including portable radio, curtains, and linoleum, cost just over £100.

Last spring Mr Laing found the ideal site—a little hollow surrounded by fields and woods near Longforgan, Perthshire. It's completely shut off, yet only a few hundred yards f...

HOLIDAYS WERE JOLLYDAYS AT BUTLIN'S. SCOTLAND'S ONLY BUTLIN'S CAMP WAS SITUATED AT HEADS OF AYR AND OPENED TO THE PUBLIC IN 1947. ADVERTISED AS PROVIDING FAMILY ENTERTAINMENT AND ACTIVITIES FOR THE EQUIVALENT OF A WEEK'S PAY, THESE CAMPS PROVIDED FUN FOR ALL - WHATEVER THE WEATHER.

EARLY CARAVAN SITES OFFERED FEW OF THE AMENITIES WHICH ARE TAKEN FOR GRANTED TODAY. NOTE THE 'PLAY AREA' ON THE RIGHT OF THIS PICTURE.

THE HEIGHT OF LUXURY IN 1961.

Teachers Not Pleased With Their Holidays

OOR WULLIE   Happy Days!

The Sunday Post 24th July 1966

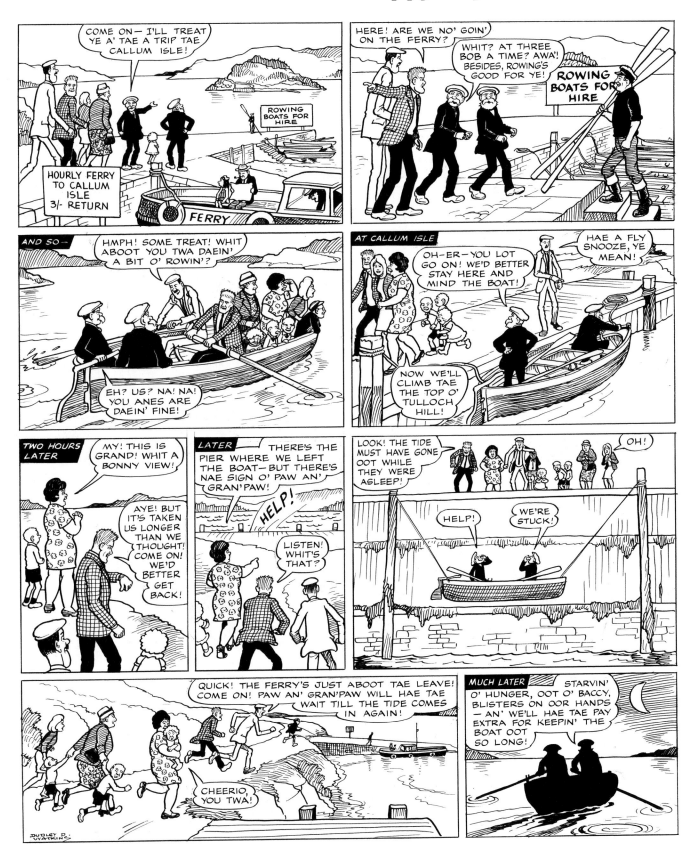

The Sunday Post 30th July 1967

OOR WULLIE   Happy Days!

The Sunday Post 25th September 1966

OOR WULLIE Happy Days!

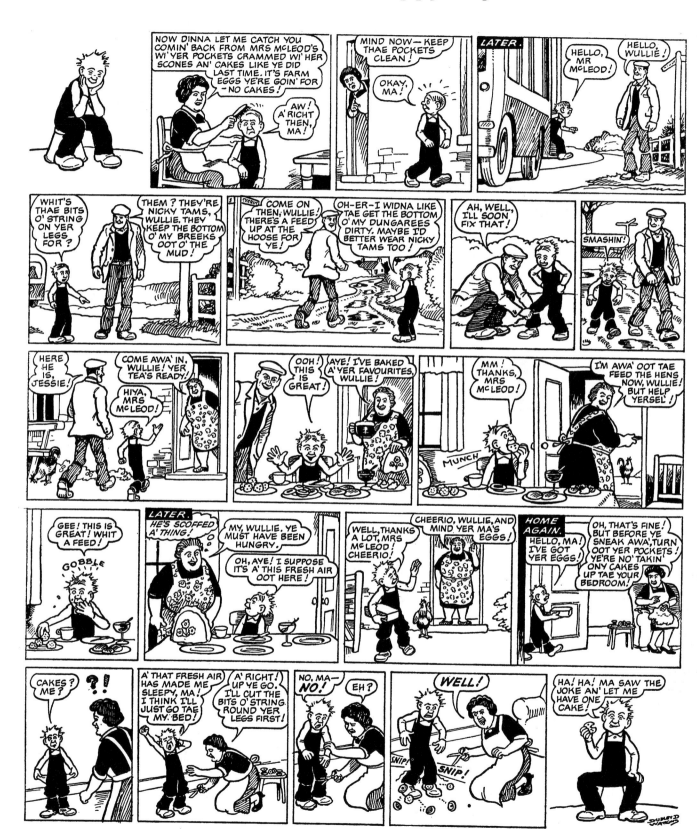

The Sunday Post 26th March 1967

THE BROONS Happy Days!

The Sunday Post 31st March 1968

Happy Days!

FOR THE CHILDREN OF THE FAMILY, HAPPY DAYS WERE USUALLY SPENT PLAYING WITH THEIR PALS – OFTEN IN THE STREET OR, IF THEY WERE LUCKY, THE NEARBY PARK. THESE CHARMING IMAGES PROVE THAT THERE WAS A LIFE BEFORE COMPUTER GAMES AND WALL-TO-WALL TV. AND THERE'S NOT AN MP3 PLAYER OR MOBILE PHONE IN SIGHT.

READY, STEADY, GO! BUT WHERE'S OOR WULLIE IN THIS CARTIE - OR BARROW - RACE IN 1955?

YOUNGSTERS WAIT PATIENTLY FOR THEIR TURN ON THE SWING. ENJOYING YOURSELF WAS A SERIOUS BUSINESS IN THE MID 50s.

Big News For Boys & Girls!

THE TOPPER

Free WITH Nº1 OF THIS GRAND FUN PAPER

THE BIG CRACK BANG

Tons Of Fun For Girls & Boys – With One Of Those Terrific Toys.

THE GREAT NEW EXTRA-BIG ALL-COLOUR ALL-FUN PAPER!

MEET THESE FUNNY FOLK AND MANY OTHERS

BERYL THE PERIL   MICKEY THE MONKEY

TREASURE ISLAND

READ THESE THRILLING STORIES

THE FIGHTING FRASERS

IN WORDS AND PICTURES.

Nº1 With Smashing Free Gift On Sale Friday 6th Feb. PRICE 3D

Prince Charles Goes To School

PRINCE CHARLES will be at school this week. His classroom is the same one at the Palace where his mother and Princess Margaret had their lessons.

His teacher, Miss Kathleen Peebles, is living at the Palace.

This week-end Prince Charles and Princess Anne are at Royal Lodge, Windsor, with the Queen Mother and Princess Margaret.

A HIGHLY CHARGED GAME OF CONKERS IN 1947. WONDER IF THEY'VE BEEN STEEPED IN VINEGAR TO TOUGHEN THEM UP. (THE CHESTNUTS, THAT IS, NOT THE BOYS.)

ROWING FOR GOLD IN 1958.

THAT'S THE WAY TO DO IT! THESE YOUNGSTERS ARE TOTALLY ENTHRALLED BY A PUNCH AND JUDY SHOW. THE POPULAR PUPPETS PROVIDED CHILDREN'S ENTERTAINMENT AT FAIRS, LOCAL SHOWS AND PARKS FOR MANY YEARS.

OOR WULLIE Happy Days!

The Sunday Post 6th August 1967

The Sunday Post 7th April 1968

The Sunday Post 21st July 1968

This final page was first published in 1954 and then reprinted on 30th November 1969, following the death of Dudley D. Watkins. It is a perfect example of the humour which has made both The Broons and Oor Wullie favourites with readers of all ages over many decades.

YOU'LL NEVER BE GLUM WI' THIS WEE CHUM!

We hope you enjoy this selection of introductory rhymes taken from some 'Oor Wullie' pages over the decades.

BADGES FROM ALL O'ER THE PLACE
GIVE OOR WULL A REAL LONG FACE.
BUT WHEN HE MEETS THIS LAD, PIERRE,
HE'S ONE UP ON HIS PALS - SO THERE!

SEE WULLIE IN HIS DUNGAREES,
HIS 'NICKY TAMS' TIED 'NEATH HIS KNEES.
WULL THINKS THEY'RE GREAT, AND NO MISTAKE.
THEY TAKE THE BISCUIT (AND THE CAKE)!

NO WONDER WULLIE'S WOEBEGONE -
HE'S UP AND OOT AT CRACK O' DAWN!
AND THAT, FOR WULLIE'S, NOT THE WAY
TO SPEND A RESTFUL HOLIDAY!

BLACK EYES ARE AWFY COMMONPLACE -
YE'LL SEE THEM OFTEN ON WULL'S FACE!
NOW PIRATES IS HIS GAME, BUT - WHY?
THERE'S MORE TO THIS THAN MEETS THE EYE!

WULLIE'S RUN NEAR AFF HIS LEGS,
PROTECTIN' WEE BIRDS AN' THEIR EGGS.
HE'S FAIR TIRED OOT, BUT NOW HE KENS
THE BEST BIRDS O' THE LOT ARE HENS.